# A Note to Parents

DK READERS is a compelling program for beginning readers, designed in conjunction with leading literacy experts, including Dr. Linda Gambrell, Distinguished Professor of Education at Clemson University. Dr. Gambrell has served as President of the National Reading Conference, the College Reading Association, and the International Reading Association.

Beautiful illustrations and superb full-color photographs combine with engaging, easy-to-read stories and informational texts to offer a fresh approach to each subject in the series. Each DK READER is guaranteed to capture a child's interest while developing his or her reading skills, general knowledge, and love of reading.

The five levels of DK READERS are aimed at different reading abilities, enabling you to choose the books that are exactly right for your child:

**Pre-level 1:** Learning to read
**Level 1:** Beginning to read
**Level 2:** Beginning to read alone
**Level 3:** Reading alone
**Level 4:** Proficient readers

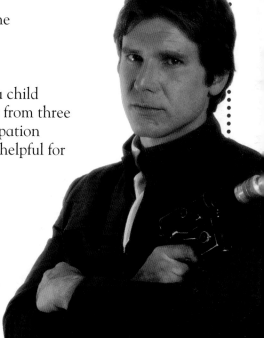

The "normal" age at which a child begins to read can be anywhere from three to eight years old. Adult participation through the lower levels is very helpful for providing encouragement, discussing storylines, and sounding out unfamiliar words.

No matter which level you select, you can be sure that you are helping your child learn to read, then read to learn!

**For Dorling Kindersley**
**Senior Editor** Laura Gilbert
**Managing Art Editor** Ron Stobbart
**Publishing Manager** Catherine Saunders
**Art Director** Lisa Lanzarini
**Associate Publisher** Simon Beecroft
**Category Publisher** Alex Allan
**Production Editor** Siu Yin Chan
**Production Controller** Rita Sinha
**Reading Consultant** Dr. Linda Gambrell

**For Lucasfilm**
**Executive Editor** J. W. Rinzler
**Art Director** Troy Alders
**Keeper of the Holocron** Leland Chee
**Director of Publishing** Carol Roeder

**Designer** Lisa Sodeau
**Editor** Lindsay Kent

First published in the United States in 2011
by DK Publishing
345 Hudson Street, New York, New York 10014
16 17 18 10 9 8 7 6 5 4

Published in Great Britain by Dorling Kinderley Limited

DK books are available at special discounts when purchased in bulk
for sales promotions, premiums, fund-raising, or educational use.
For details, contact:
DK Publishing Special Markets
345 Hudson Street
New York, New York 10014
SpecialSales@dk.com

A catalog record for this book is available
from the Library of Congress.

ISBN: 978-0-7566-8252-1 (Paperback)
ISBN: 978-0-7566-8251-4 (Hardcover)

Reproduced by Media Development
and Printing Ltd., UK
Printed and bound in China

**www.dk.com**
**www.starwars.com**

A WORLD OF IDEAS:
**SEE ALL THERE IS TO KNOW**

# Contents

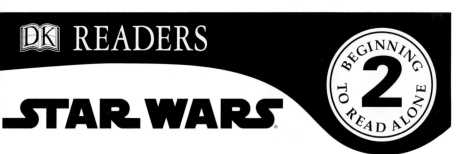

**DK READERS**

BEGINNING **2** TO READ ALONE

**STAR WARS®**

# The Adventures of Han Solo

Written by
Lindsay Kent

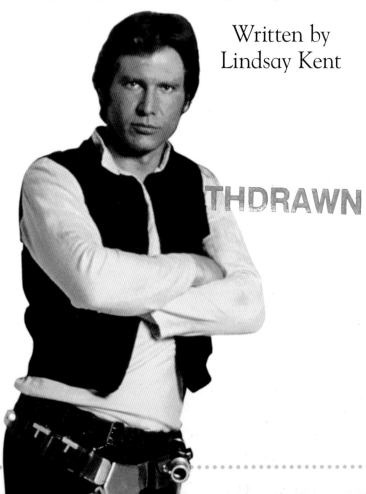

THDRAWN

This is Han Solo.
Han is a great pilot and
a skilled fighter.
He is also very smart.

Han fights for the Rebel Alliance.
He is a General. The Rebel
Alliance is a group of people who
fight against the Empire.
They think the ruler of the Empire
treats the people of the
galaxy badly.

**Ruthless leader**
Emperor Palpatine
is the evil ruler of
the Galactic
Empire.

Han is a very brave man.
He helps the Rebel Alliance
destroy the Death Star.
During the battle
Han flies his spaceship,
called the *Millennium Falcon.*
He fights the Emperor's spaceships.
Han was given a special medal for
his bravery.

**Death Star**

The Death Star is a big space station created by the Empire. It has a powerful weapon that can destroy an entire planet.

Chewbacca is a Wookiee.
He is very tall. He is covered in
long fur. He is Han's best friend.

Han calls Chewbacca "Chewie"
for short. Wookiees speak a
language called Shyriiwook
(SHE-REE-WOOK).
Han can speak Shyriiwook because
he was raised by a
Wookiee called
Dewlanna.

**Co-pilot**
Chewie helps Han
fly their starship,
the *Millennium Falcon*.

Han's spaceship is called
the *Millennium Falcon.*
He won it in a game
of sabacc.

The ship is very old. Sometimes
Han and Chewie have to repair
it—even in the middle of a battle!

Han and Chewie have added
a hyperdrive to the ship.
The hyperdrive makes the ship fly
very fast. This has allowed Han
and Chewie to escape from
danger many times!

Han used to be a pirate.
He was one of the best smugglers
in the galaxy!
Han smuggled materials in secret
compartments in the floor of the
*Millennium Falcon.*

**Imperial stormtroopers**

Stormtroopers are soldiers who fight for the Empire.

The compartments are useful when Han and his friends need to hide from stormtroopers!

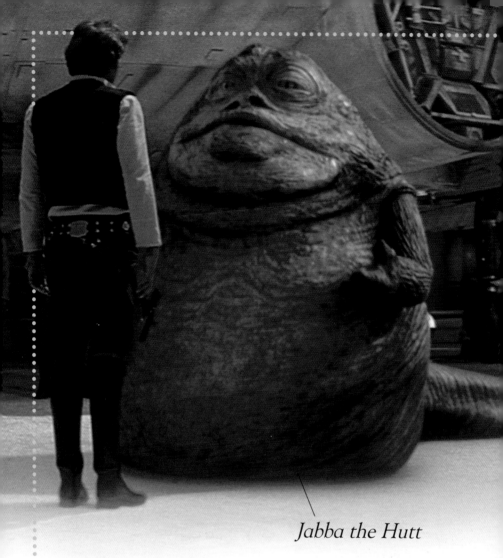

*Jabba the Hutt*

Oh no—it's Jabba the Hutt!
Jabba is a powerful crime lord.
Han used to smuggle for Jabba.
On one trip Han lost Jabba's
cargo and Jabba wasn't happy!

**Bounty hunter**
Greedo is a
bounty hunter
who is searching
for Han.

Now Han owes Jabba money.
Jabba hires bounty hunters to
search for Han and capture him.
The reward is so big that bounty
hunters from all over the galaxy
look for him.

Han needs money quickly so he
can pay back Jabba the Hutt.
He hears that a Jedi Knight
named Obi-Wan Kenobi and
his friend Luke Skywalker need
transport to a planet called
Alderaan (ALL-DER-ARN).

**Jedi Knights**

Jedi Knights are warriors who belong to the Jedi Order. They fight for good and help to maintain order in the galaxy.

Han and Chewbacca agree to fly them there if they pay Han and Chewie a lot of money.

This is Luke Skywalker.
He is a Jedi Knight.
Luke and Han become
good friends and try to
look after each other.
Luke becomes lost
on an icy planet
called Hoth.
The cold
weather is very
dangerous,
but Han goes
out to search
for his
friend.

Luke is hurt when Han finds him.
Han keeps him warm until
help arrives.

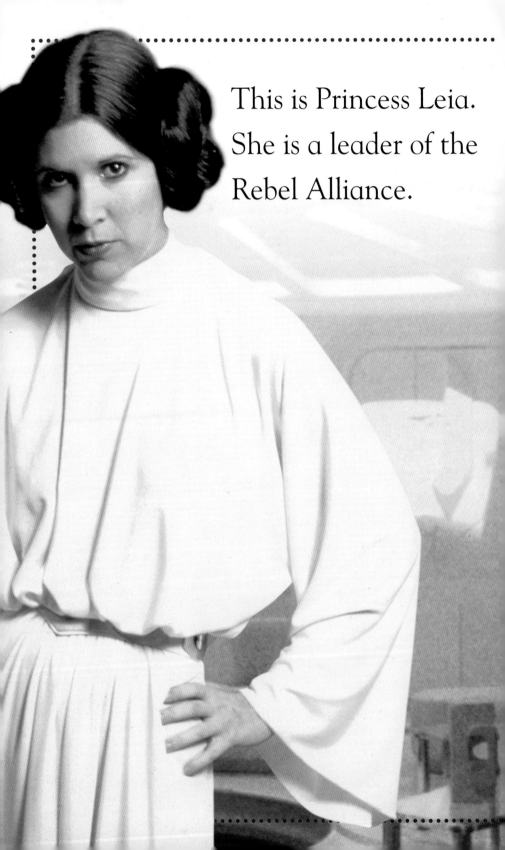

This is Princess Leia. She is a leader of the Rebel Alliance.

Han meets Leia for the first time when he helps to rescue her from the Imperial Death Star. At first Han and Leia don't like each other, but soon they fall in love.

This is Lando Calrissian. He is Han's friend. Lando is in charge of a place called Cloud City. Han, Leia, and Chewie go to Cloud City when they are trying to escape from Darth Vader.

Lando says that he will hide them from the Emperor's troops, but it is a trap! Darth Vader is already waiting in Cloud City to capture them. Lando doesn't want to trick Han, but Darth Vader forces him to.

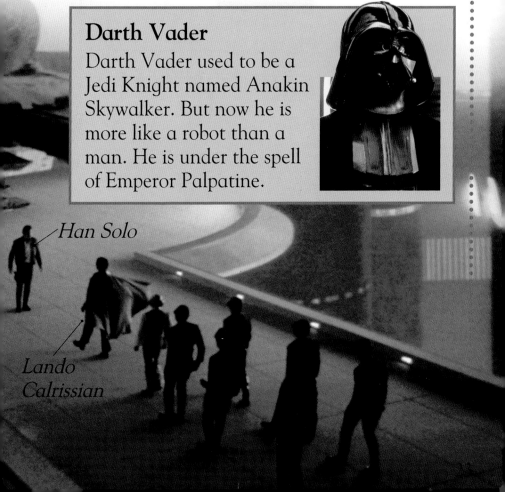

**Darth Vader**
Darth Vader used to be a Jedi Knight named Anakin Skywalker. But now he is more like a robot than a man. He is under the spell of Emperor Palpatine.

Han Solo

Lando
Calrissian

Han's adventures are very dangerous. On one adventure Han lands his ship in the stomach of a giant space slug by mistake! He manages to escape from its jaws just in time.

## Dangerous mission

On another mission Han and his friends are trapped in a smelly garbage compactor on the Death Star. Luckily two droids named C-3PO and R2-D2 help them before they are squashed!

Sometimes Han can't escape from tricky situations. He is captured by Darth Vader in Cloud City and is frozen in carbonite. Han is still alive, but he is frozen solid and cannot move.

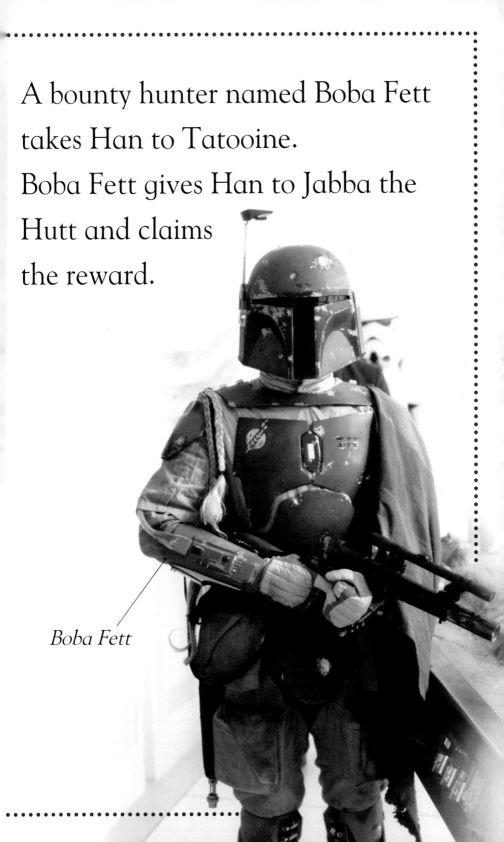

A bounty hunter named Boba Fett
takes Han to Tatooine.
Boba Fett gives Han to Jabba the
Hutt and claims
the reward.

*Boba Fett*

Watch out!
This creature is called the Sarlacc.
Its tentacles can grab hold
of anyone who is nearby.
The Sarlacc pulls them into its
mouth and digests them for years.

**A good friend**
Han saves Lando
Calrissian from
falling into the
mouth of the
Sarlacc.

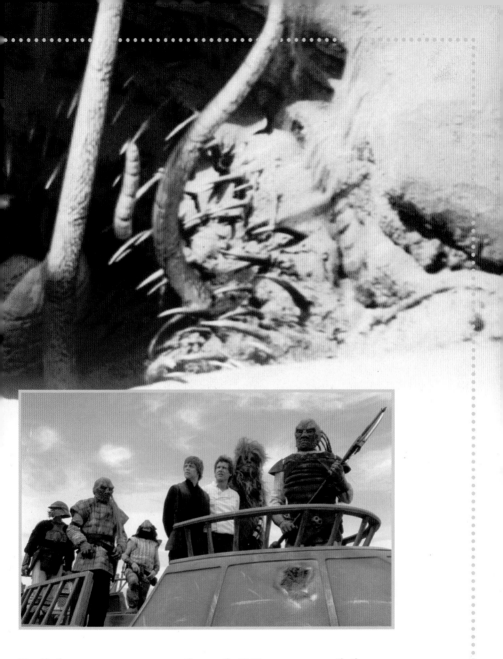

Jabba tries to feed Han and his friends to the Sarlacc, but they destroy Jabba and escape.

Han has flown from one side of the galaxy to the other. He has seen many unusual creatures. On the Moon of Endor, Han meets Ewoks.

Ewoks are very small, but they are also brave and strong.

They capture Han and the Rebels, but later they all become friends.

The Ewoks help the Rebels to defeat the Emperor's troops in the Battle of Endor. They celebrate their victory and the end of the Empire with fireworks and dancing.

# Glossary

**Bounty hunters**
People who look for and capture people for a reward.

**Compactor**
Something that makes garbage smaller by squashing it.

**Compartments**
Small spaces used to store things.

**Co-pilot**
Someone who helps a pilot to fly a spaceship.

**Crime lord**
The boss of a criminal gang.

**Digests**
The way the body breaks food down into smaller parts so it can be used for energy.

**Jedi**
People who can sense the energy created by all living things. This energy is called the Force.

**Pirate**
Someone who raids and steals from spaceships.

**Sabacc**
Sabacc is a card game. Players bet with money or personal belongings.

**Smuggler**
Someone who takes goods to a country or planet illegally.

**Tentacle**
Part of an animal that is long and used to grab hold of things.

**Victory**
A win in a battle or a game.